ENCOUNTER

experiencing God in the everyday

mark hart

_____'s Workbook

YOUR NAME

ASCENSION

West Chester, Pennsylvania

Nihil obstat: Reverend Robert A. Pesarchick, S.T.D.
                   Censor Librorum
                   January 3, 2013

Imprimatur: +Most Reverend Charles J. Chaput, O.F.M. Cap.
                   Archbishop of Philadelphia
                   January 24, 2013

Encounter is a resource of *The Great Adventure* Catholic Bible Study Program.

Jeff Cavins, General Editor, *The Great Adventure,* and creator of the *Bible Timeline* Learning System.

Sarah Christmyer, Editor, *The Great Adventure.*

Mark Hart, Author and Presenter, *Encounter: Experiencing God in the Everyday.*

Ascension
Post Office Box 1990
West Chester, PA 19380
1-800-376-0520
ascensionpress.com

Cover Design: Devin Schadt

Printed in the United States of America

ISBN: 978-1-935940-48-7

TABLE OF CONTENTS

Welcome

There are a lot of ways you can get to know people, but nothing works like sitting with someone one-on-one and talking together. That person can't really know you, either, until you share from your heart.

There is one important exception, someone who knows all about you and loves you more than life itself. No, not Santa Claus, and not your parents. It's God, the author of your life. That's right, God is the author, and you are a character in his story. And if you really want to know yourself, the best and fastest way to do that is to get to know the one who created you.

The Bible is a great way to get to know God and the kind of Father he is. You'll also get to know a lot of his children. Everyone you encounter in the Bible is worth learning from in some way. You'll soon realize that living as a Christian is not so much about "finding yourself" as it is about finding and unleashing Christ's power within you. The more you recognize God's presence in your life, the better you'll be able to share his love with others.

The secret to a joyful life and a hope-filled future isn't about figuring out tomorrow; it's about listening to God today. God, the author of life, has something to say to you through the brothers and sisters who went before you. So take a deep breath and turn the page—it's story time!

God bless you!

Mark Hart

Mark Hart

Session One

• AN INTRODUCTION TO THE BIBLE

You'll open a lot of books in your lifetime—textbooks, yearbooks, comic books, maybe art and poetry books. You already know how much you *love* lugging around textbooks in your backpack for studying. But did a textbook ever change your life?

On the other hand, maybe you're an avid reader, and your room is full of books. Or maybe you prefer to read everything on a screen. Whatever the case, there is one book that is different from any other. It's the best-selling book in history, published in every language on the planet, and available in almost every corner of the earth (even in places where it is still illegal). That book is the Bible.

The Bible is different from any other book you'll ever read. It's not just words *about* God. Scripture is the Word *of* God, and that difference is huge.

Other books might help you learn about the Bible, like this study will. But nothing, no other book, no study, no pamphlet, will ever give you what the Bible can … for when you read the Bible yourself, something amazing happens.

God blesses you in a very special way, and his life (grace) fills you in a new way.

Forget what you've heard or learned about the Bible in the past. Forget how you felt in the past about reading Scripture on your own. As we begin, ask the Holy Spirit, the actual author of Scripture, to open your mind, your eyes, your ears, and your heart as we move forward, now. Your life is about to change for the better.

Let's have some fun …

VERSE TO REMEMBER

" … you will know the truth, and the truth will make you free."

POP QUIZ!

How many random facts and details can you remember off the top of your head?

1. Name the heroes in *The Avengers*.

2. Name five Disney/Pixar movies.

3. Name three shows on the Disney channel.

4. Name three shows on MTV.

5. Name the seven dwarves from *Snow White*.

6. Name the first five books of the Bible.

7. Name five prophets in the Old Testament.

8. Name the four Gospels.

9. Name the twelve apostles.

10. Name the seven sacraments of the Catholic Church.

Creation ➤ 2000 BC ➤ 1700 BC ➤ 1280 BC ➤ 1240 BC ➤ 1050 BC

 EARLY WORLD Genesis 1-11

 PATRIARCHS Genesis 12-50

 EGYPT & EXODUS Exodus

 DESERT WANDERINGS Numbers

CONQUEST & JUDGES Joshua Judges

 ROYAL KINGDOM I & II Samuel I Kings 1-11

Session 1: Breaking It Down

1.   What does the word "Bible" mean?_____

2.   Why did God give us the Bible?_____

3.   How many books are in the Catholic Bible?
     a. Old Testament: _____   b. New Testament: _____

4.   Which books are the most important books in the Bible?_____

5.   What does the word "gospel" mean?_____

6.   What's the best book a Catholic can read along with the Bible?_____

7.   Why is owning a Bible such a huge responsibility?_____

     _____

BRAIN TEASER

If you had a ton of rosaries and a ton of Bibles, which would weigh more?

Neither, they'd both weigh a ton.

30 BC ➤ 722 BC ➤ 540 BC ➤ 167 BC ➤ 0 ➤ 33 AD ➤

| DIVIDED KINGDOM | EXILE | RETURN | MACCABEAN REVOLT | MESSIANIC FULFILLMENT | THE CHURCH |
| I Kings 12-22 II Kings | II Kings | Ezra Nehemiah | I Maccabees | Luke | Acts |

QUOTES ABOUT SCRIPTURE FROM THE SAINTS

"The study of inspired Scripture is the chief way of finding our duty."

-St. Basil the Great

"The Church of Christ has always, and never fails in, the right understanding of Scripture, so far as is necessary for our salvation." -St. Thomas More

"Ignorance of Scripture is ignorance of Christ."

-St. Jerome

"All the troubles of the Church, all the evils in the world, flow from this source: that men do not by clear and sound knowledge and serious consideration penetrate into the truths of Sacred Scripture." -St. Teresa of Avila

"Divine Scripture is the feast of wisdom, and the individual books are the various dishes." -St. Ambrose of Milan

"Study your heart in the light of the Holy Scriptures, and you will know therein who you were, who you are, and who you ought to be." -St. Fulgentius of Ruspe

"Each man marvels to find in the divine Scriptures truths that he himself thought out."

-St. Thomas Aquinas

"The Bible is a letter from Almighty God to his creatures."

-Pope St. Gregory the Great

"God's word is so rich that it is a treasury of every good; from it flow faith, hope, love, and all the virtues, the many gifts of the Spirit." -St. Lawrence of Brindisi

"If you believe what you like in the gospels, and reject what you don't like, it is not the gospel you believe, but yourself." -St. Augustine

"The holy and inspired Scriptures are sufficient of themselves for the preaching of the Truth." -St. Athanasius

Session Two

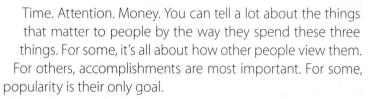

● EARLY WORLD

Book: Genesis 1–11

Time. Attention. Money. You can tell a lot about the things that matter to people by the way they spend these three things. For some, it's all about how other people view them. For others, accomplishments are most important. For some, popularity is their only goal.

So what is most important to you? What makes you, *you*?

- What is the most important thing in your life? Who are the most important people? Does your time reflect both?

- Where does God fit in? Just like people put their time and money into different things, people also put their faith into different things.

As you'll learn in this session, right from the beginning of Creation, God is blessing us. He wants to be in relationship with us. He is generous and loving. The Creator is creative, and he has style on top of it.

(Just look at the giraffe or the platypus—God has style!)

As we move through these first few chapters of the Bible together, ask yourself what—and, more importantly, who—matters most to you in your life right now. Think about where all those people and things come from. Consider what you'd do if every *thing* in your life was taken away; would you still be happy? Stop and reflect on what God wants *for* you before you think about what he might want *from* you.

God doesn't just love you. He *likes* you. God rejoices in you. He doesn't look at you and see "all you aren't"; God looks at you and sees his own beautiful creation. He sees all that you can be and all that he designed you to be.

VERSE TO REMEMBER

"God created man in his own image, in the image of God he created him; male and female he created them."

Genesis 1:27

5

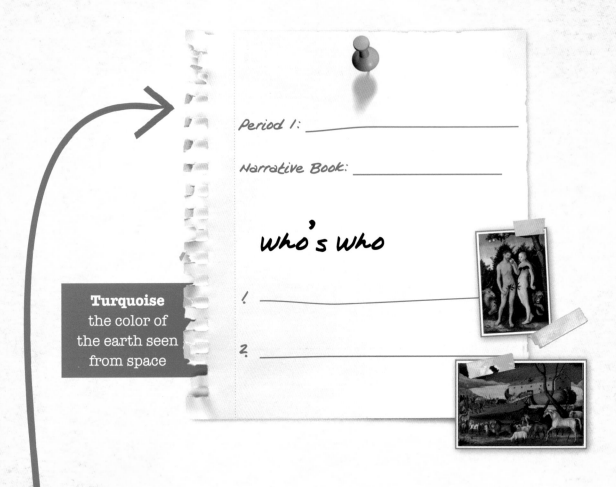

Period 1: _____

Narrative Book: _____

who's who

1. _____

2. _____

Turquoise
the color of
the earth seen
from space

DID YOU KNOW?

Noah's ark was 300 cubits long. Since a cubit is about eighteen inches, that makes the ark about 450 feet long or roughly the size of one-and-a-half football fields.

Creation ┈┈┈┈┈► 2000 BC   1700 BC   1280 BC   1240 BC   1050 BC

EARLY WORLD
Genesis 1-11

PATRIARCHS
Genesis 12-50

EGYPT & EXODUS
Exodus

DESERT WANDERINGS
Numbers

CONQUEST & JUDGES
Joshua
Judges

ROYAL KINGDOM
I & II Samuel
I Kings 1-11

Session 2: Breaking It Down

1. What does the title "Genesis" mean?_____

2. What do the two different accounts of Creation teach us?

    a. Genesis 1: _____

    b. Genesis 2: _____

3. What made Adam and Eve so different from the animals?_____
    _____

4. What is a "covenant"?_____

5. What is "sin" and what does sin "do"?_____

6. What about Cain disappointed God so much?_____

7. How long did it rain when Noah was in the ark?_____

Q: Why did Noah have to discipline the chickens on the ark?

A: Because they were using "fowl" language.

"God created everything out of nothing, and he created you with a purpose."

—Mark Hart

30 BC ▸ 722 BC ▸ 540 BC ▸ 167 BC ▸ 0 ▸ 33 AD

DIVIDED KINGDOM
I Kings 12-22
II Kings

EXILE
II Kings

RETURN
Ezra
Nehemiah

MACCABEAN REVOLT
I Maccabees

MESSIANIC FULFILLMENT
Luke

THE CHURCH
Acts

THE DIVINE DESIGNER

Some people like to believe there is no God, and that we are all just a result of a random explosion (or the Big Bang).

When you take a closer look at life and creation, however, you'll notice that we are amazingly intricate creatures living on an incredibly complex and perfectly designed planet.

Yes, you are God's walking, talking masterpiece!

- Your body has sixty trillion to ninety trillion living cells—of about 200 different types![1]
- A piece of human bone the size of a matchbox can support 19,000 pounds.[2]
- Skin is the largest organ of the body—in one year you will shed about eight pounds of skin. [3]
- The human eye has 120 million rods and six million to seven million cones.[4]
- Your kidney has a million individual filters.[5]

But that's not all—God designed the whole earth with infinite attention to detail.

- The earth's axis is tipped at a perfect 23.5 degrees, which gives us our seasons. Anything more or less and we wouldn't have seasons—or even be able to survive, for that matter.[6]
- Each winter about one septillion (1,000,000,000,000,000,000,000,000 or a trillion trillion) snow crystals drop from the sky.[7]
- A huge, underground river runs beneath the Nile, containing six times more water than the Nile itself.[8]
- About eighty percent of the earth's atmosphere is actually nitrogen. Most of the rest is oxygen.[9]
- On average, the oceans on earth are 2.65 miles deep.[10]
- About one-third of the earth's land surface is desert.[11]
- The total water supply of the world is 326 million cubic miles (one cubic mile of water equals more than one trillion gallons).[12]
- There are 200 billion to 400 billion stars in our galaxy.[13]

Session Three

- PATRIARCHS
- EGYPT & EXODUS (PART 1)

Books: Genesis 12–50, Exodus

Nobody's family is perfect. Sure, you might look around at your friends' families and wish you had one like theirs (or thank God that you don't). The thing is, it's important to look at your own family in order to love and understand them as God calls you to do.

Do you spend more time upset about how things are or on working to love your family members better? Do you focus more on what you don't have in your family or on thanking God for all you *do* have?

As you'll hear in this session, families have been messed up for thousands of years. Sometimes it's their fault and sometimes it's not, but God is always reaching out and encouraging us to get better.

God isn't far away. These chapters remind us that God is very much present in our day-to-day lives; sometimes we just have to look harder to find him. Sometimes we have to be more patient, too.

When things don't go your way, do you trust God? Do you blame God? Do you doubt his love?

You're about to meet characters who did all three of these things. You can learn from all three types of responses. The choices you make will help determine the kind of life you are going to have: a life filled with joy or a life filled with sorrow.

The choice is yours. So, let's get to it!

VERSE TO REMEMBER

"The LORD will fight for you, and you have only to be still."

Period 2: _____

Narrative Book: _____

who's who

1. _____

2. _____

3. _____

4. _____

Burgundy
the blood
of the
patriarchs

Period 3: _____ Part 1

Narrative Book: _____

who's who

5. _____

Red
the Red Sea

2000 BC ········➤ 1700 BC ········➤ 1280 BC

Creation ········➤

1240 BC ········➤ 1050 BC ········➤

EARLY WORLD	PATRIARCHS	EGYPT & EXODUS	DESERT WANDERINGS	CONQUEST & JUDGES	ROYAL KINGDOM
Genesis 1-11	Genesis 12-50	Exodus	Numbers	Joshua Judges	I & II Samuel I Kings 1-11

session 3: Breaking It Down

1.   Why does God change someone's name?_____

2.   What's so "funny" about Isaac's name?_____

3.   What did Jacob do to his brother, Esau?_____

4.   How many sons did Jacob have?_____

5.   What did Joseph's older brothers do?_____

6.   What did Moses ask God?_____

7.   How did God show his power over creation and the false gods of Egypt?

_____

Q: Where is the first tennis match mentioned in the Bible?
A: When Joseph served in Pharaoh's court.

DID YOU KNOW?

Moses didn't get his name from his parents but, rather, from Pharaoh's daughter who fished him out of the Nile (Exodus 2:10). It's probably better for Moses; his parents' names were Amram (his father) and Jochebed (his mother).

30 BC ----- ▸ 722 BC ----- ▸ 540 BC ----- ▸ 167 BC ----- ▸ 0 ----- ▸ 33 AD ----- ▸

| DIVIDED KINGDOM I Kings 12-22 II Kings | EXILE II Kings | RETURN Ezra Nehemiah | MACCABEAN REVOLT I Maccabees | MESSIANIC FULFILLMENT Luke | THE CHURCH Acts |

JESUS' FAMILY TREE

God was the Father of Adam, and **Adam** the father of Seth, and Seth the father of ... Lamech, and Lamech the father of **Noah**, and Noah the father of Shem, and Shem the father of ... Terah, the father of **Abraham**.[1] "Abraham was the father of **Isaac**, and Isaac the father of **Jacob**, and Jacob the father of **Judah** and his brothers, and Judah the father of Perez and Zerah by Tamar, and Perez the father of Hezron, and Hezron the father of Ram, and Ram the father of Amminadab, and Amminadab the father of Nahshon, and Nahshon the father of Salmon, and Salmon the father of Boaz by Rahab, and **Boaz** the father of Obed by Ruth, and Obed the father of **Jesse**, and Jesse the father of **David** the king. And David was the father of **Solomon** by the wife of Uriah, and Solomon the father of Rehoboam, and Rehoboam the father of Abijah, and Abijah the father of Asa, and Asa the father of Jehoshaphat, and Jehoshaphat the father of Joram, and Joram the father of Uzziah, and Uzziah the father of Jotham, and Jotham the father of Ahaz, and Ahaz the father of Hezekiah, and Hezekiah the father of Manasseh, and Manasseh the father of Amos, and Amos the father of **Josiah**, and Josiah the father of Jechoniah and his brothers, at the time of the deportation to Babylon. And after the deportation to Babylon: Jechoniah was the father of She-alti-el, and She-alti-el the father of **Zerubbabel**, and Zerubbabel the father of Abiud, and Abiud the father of Eliakim, and Eliakim the father of Azor, and Azor the father of Zadok, and Zadok the father of Achim, and Achim the father of Eliud, and Eliud the father of Eleazar, and Eleazar the father of Matthan, and Matthan the father of Jacob, and Jacob the father of **Joseph the husband of Mary**, of whom **Jesus** was born, who is called **Christ**."[2]

[1] Adapted from Luke 3:34-38. See Genesis 5–11 for Old Testament genealogy prior to Abraham. Note: The Hebrew word translated "father" sometimes indicates a more distant paternal relationship (e.g., grandfather or great-grandfather).

[2] Matthew 1:1-16

Session Four

- EGYPT & EXODUS (PART 2)
- DESERT WANDERINGS
- CONQUEST & JUDGES

Books: Exodus, Numbers, Joshua, Judges

God is many things. He is perfect love, unending mercy, unparalleled compassion, and absolute justice.

God is not, however, a genie … no matter how many people treat him like one.

Countless people go to God only when they want or need something. Now, God is happy to listen to those requests, but he offers (and wants) so much more! God wants you to share your day with him, to invite him into the good and the bad parts. God wants you to thank him when things go well and seek him when things don't turn out as planned.

Sadly, God often is seen more as an emergency back-up plan than as a best friend or loving Father.

Take a minute to think about all the ways God has blessed you. You might even want to write them down here.

_____

_____

_____

Next, thank God for all of those things (and people). Okay, keep this list somewhere safe, and the next time something goes terribly wrong in your life, refer to it.

If the people you're about to study had just remembered all that God had done for them—all the ways he had blessed them—things would have turned out even better in their lives.

Don't ever make the mistake of thinking God doesn't care about you. God is love, and he loves you far more than you can imagine. He's constantly showing it, but if we're too busy thinking up "three new wishes," we'll miss all the blessings he has already granted.

VERSE TO REMEMBER

" … the LORD sees not as man sees; man looks on the outward appearance, but the LORD looks on the heart."

_____

Period 3: _____   Part 2

Narrative Book: _____

Red
the Red Sea

who's who

1. _____

2. _____

Period 4: _____

Narrative Book: _____

who's who

3. Moses _____

Tan
the color
of the
desert

4. Aaron _____

5. _____

1700 BC ········▶ 1280 BC ········▶ 1240 BC ········▶ 1250 BC

Creation ········▶ 2000 BC ········

EARLY WORLD	PATRIARCHS	EGYPT & EXODUS	DESERT WANDERINGS	CONQUEST & JUDGES	ROYAL KINGDOM
Genesis 1-11	Genesis 12-50	Exodus	Numbers	Joshua Judges	I & II Samuel I Kings 1-11

Session 4: Breaking It Down

1. Where did God give Moses the Ten Commandments?_____

2. Which tribe became God's priests?_____

3. How long would the Israelites have to wander in the desert?_____

4. What did Moses do that got him in trouble?_____
_____

5. How were the snake-bitten Israelites healed?_____
_____

6. Who was Moses' second-in-command? _____Joshua_____

7. What is the name of the Bible's most famous strong man? _____Samson_____

Period 5: _____

Narrative Books: _____

Green
the green hills of Canaan

Who's Who

6. Joshua _____

7. _____

8. _____

DIVIDED KINGDOM
I Kings 12-22
II Kings

EXILE
II Kings

RETURN
Ezra
Nehemiah

MACCABEAN REVOLT
I Maccabees

MESSIANIC FULFILLMENT
Luke

THE CHURCH
Acts

LIST THE TEN COMMANDMENTS

When God gave Moses the Ten Commandments atop Mt. Sinai, he was doing more than giving all of us a list of "rules" to follow.

God wants us to be with him for eternity in heaven. The commandments are God's way of helping us live holier, more selfless lives—the commandments help us to become saints.

You probably know most (if not all) of the commandments. Do you know them in order?

List as many of the Ten Commandments as you can below, from memory.

The Ten Commandments (Exodus 20):

1. _____

2. _____

3. _____

4. _____

5. _____

6. _____

7. _____

8. _____

9. _____

10. _____

How'd you do?

Turn to page 36 to find out.

Session Five

- ROYAL KINGDOM
- DIVIDED KINGDOM

Books: 1&2 Samuel, 1&2 Kings

Have you ever said to yourself, "*If I could just* (insert desired thing here) … *then I'd be happy.*"

Some people insert "be popular" or "become famous." Some people say "be smarter" or "be more athletic." I used to say "grow taller" and "get better-looking." My acne was so bad at one point I didn't even want to go to school. I was so stressed about how I compared to others, that it affected everything about me—what I wore, what music I listened to, and even what sports and activities I took part in.

I was more worried about how others saw me than I was about what God thought of me.

I wish I'd read these chapters we're about to walk through when I was in middle school. They remind us about what matters most. They echo what we learned in those first couple of sessions of the Timeline, about where our worth comes from and, more to the point, *who* it comes from.

This session will remind you, too, that you are capable of way more than you might think … as long as you keep God first in your life.

No mountain is too tall, no fear too big, no opponent too scary, if God is in your corner.

We're also going to see what happens when we put God second, third, or last. We'll see how badly things go when we rely too much on our own talents and skills and not on the one who gave them to us.

Buckle up, brothers and sisters—this session has more drama than any reality show.

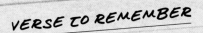

VERSE TO REMEMBER

"*Before I formed you in the womb I knew you, and before you were born I consecrated you …*"

session 5:
Breaking It Down

1. What was the name of Israel's first king? _saul_____

2. What was David's first teenage job? _____

3. What army did Goliath fight for? _____

4. What friend did David betray? _____

5. Which king built God's Temple? _____

6. When did the kingdom divide into two? _____

7. What does the word "prophet" mean? _____

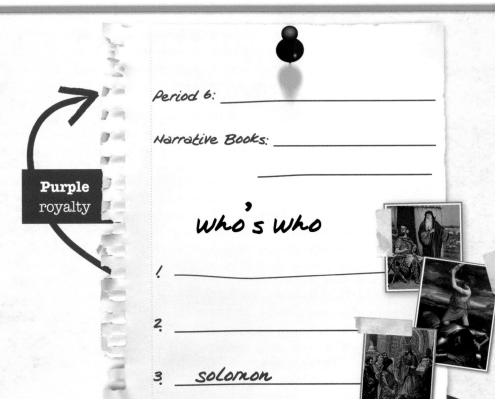

Purple
royalty

Period 6: _____

Narrative Books: _____

_____

Who's Who

1. _____

2. _____

3. _solomon_____

1250 BC

Creation → 2000 BC → 1700 BC → 1280 BC → 1240 BC →

EARLY WORLD
Genesis 1-11

EGYPT & EXODUS
Exodus

PATRIARCHS
Genesis 12-50

DESERT WANDERINGS
Numbers

CONQUEST & JUDGES
Joshua
Judges

ROYAL KINGDOM
I & II Samuel
I Kings 1-11

Period 7: _____

Narrative Books: _____

_____

who's who

Black Israel's darkest period

4. _____

5. _____

6. _____

7. _____

DID YOU KNOW?

King Solomon imported peacocks to decorate his palace (1 Kings 10:22). Throw pillows probably would have been less messy.

DIVIDED KINGDOM
I Kings 12-22
II Kings

30 BC   722 BC   540 BC   167 BC   0   33 AD

EXILE	RETURN	MACCABEAN REVOLT	MESSIANIC FULFILLMENT	THE CHURCH
II Kings	Ezra Nehemiah	I Maccabees	Luke	Acts

THE DIVIDED KINGDOM
(930 BC)

Sidon •

Mediterranean Sea

Tyre •

Dan ✦

Sea of Galilee

Yarmuk River

Jordan River

NORTHERN KINGDOM

(TEN TRIBES)

Samaria •

ISRAEL

Joppa •

✦ **Bethel**

TEMPLE — ✦
Jerusalem

Dead Sea

Arnon River

Gaza •

MOAB

PHILISTIA

JUDAH

SOUTHERN KINGDOM

(TWO TRIBES)

EGYPT

EDOM

Approximate Boundary

✦ Centers of Worship

Session Six

- EXILE
- RETURN
- MACCABEAN REVOLT

Books: 2 Kings, Ezra, Nehemiah, 1 Maccabees

You'll have a lot of different types of friends in your lifetime. Some you'll have for life, others for a shorter time. You'll have friendships that fade as soon as bad times happen, and friendships that withstand just about anything. The key is to find people who build you up, not tear you down.

This session is going to reveal a lot about what it means to be faithful—to God, to family, and to friends.

The best gift you can ever give someone else is to lead that person's soul closer to God. It's the only gift that keeps giving, for eternity. Stop and think about your life for a moment. Do most of your friends lead you closer to God or further away from his love?

Now ask yourself what kind of friend you are. Do you lead your friends—through your words and your actions—closer to God or further away from him?

These aren't stupid questions, and they aren't for immature souls. These realities matter in life. What kind of friends you choose to hang out with and the kind of friend you choose to be makes all the difference in this world … and in the next.

We're about to see what it means to be a *faithful* friend. The book of Sirach says that when you find a faithful friend, "you find a treasure" (Sirach 6:14, NAB). These chapters will affirm that truth and challenge your own friendships, if you let them.

Let's see how we measure up to those who went before us and did it right.

VERSE TO REMEMBER

"… the joy of the LORD is your strength."

Period 8: _____

Narrative Book: _____

who's who

1. _____

Baby Blue
Judah
"singing
the blues"
in Baby-lon

Yellow
Judah
returning
home to
brighter days

Period 9: _____

Narrative Books: _____

_____

who's who

2. _____

3. Nehemiah _____

4. _____

Creation ➤ 2000 BC ➤ 1700 BC ➤ 1280 BC ➤ 1240 BC ➤ 1050 BC

EARLY WORLD	PATRIARCHS	EGYPT & EXODUS	DESERT WANDERINGS	CONQUEST & JUDGES	ROYAL KINGDOM
Genesis 1-11	Genesis 12-50	Exodus	Numbers	Joshua Judges	I & II Samuel I Kings 1-11

session 6:
Breaking It Down

1. How did the Persian king try to torture Daniel's friends?_____

2. Where did God save Daniel's life?_____

3. Who was the Bible's first "beauty queen"?_____

4. What message does God give to King Cyrus?_____

5. a. What job does Zerubbabel do? _____

   b. How about Nehemiah?_____

6. Why is Ezra so important?_____

   _____

Orange
Fire in the oil lamps in the purified temple

Period 10: _____

Narrative Book: _____

who's who

5. _Judas Maccabeus_

6. _Simon Maccabeus_

722 BC — 722 BC — 167 BC — 0

30 BC — 33 AD

DIVIDED KINGDOM
I Kings 12-22
II Kings

EXILE
II Kings

RETURN
Ezra
Nehemiah

MACCABEAN REVOLT
I Maccabees

MESSIANIC FULFILLMENT
Luke

THE CHURCH
Acts

MAJOR BIBLICAL EVENTS: OLD TESTAMENT REVIEW

An *Encounter* Cheat Sheet

Everything that happens in the Bible is important, but there are some events in the Old Testament that you might want to be able to find quickly so you can study or read them on your own.

Creation, Adam and Eve (Genesis 1–3)

Noah's Ark (Genesis 6–9)

Tower of Babel (Genesis 11:1-9)

The Destruction of Sodom and Gomorrah (Genesis 19)

Abraham Sacrifices Isaac (Genesis 22:1-19)

Jacob's Ladder (Genesis 28)

The Twelve Sons of Jacob, Joseph's Rise to Power (Genesis 35–47)

The Burning Bush (Exodus 3)

The Ten Plagues (Exodus 7–12)

The Crossing of the Red Sea (Exodus 15)

The Ten Commandments (Exodus 20)

The Battle of Jericho (Joshua 6)

The Story of Ruth and Boaz (The Book of Ruth)

Samson the Judge (Judges 13–16)

David and Goliath (1 Samuel 17)

Jonah and the Whale (Jonah 1–2)

Elijah on Mount Carmel (1 Kings 18)

Esther and the King (The Book of Esther)

Daniel and the Lion's Den (Daniel 6)

Maccabean Revolt (1 Maccabees 1–4)

Session Seven

• MESSIANIC FULFILLMENT

Book: Luke

What do you believe about Jesus? What difference does it make in your life? These are the two most important decisions you will ever make.

That is absolutely true and important, so I'll say it again:

What you believe about Jesus, and what difference that makes in your life, are the two most important decisions you will ever make.

No other major religious leader (aside from some minor, crazy people) ever claimed to be God like Jesus Christ did. Some have claimed to have special insights into God, or to have spoken to God, or to be sent by God, but none of them actually claimed *to be God*.

Only the carpenter from Nazareth did that … and he died for it.

He rose because of it, too, and that fact changes everything.

Some people will say Jesus was a nice guy or a good teacher, but they won't admit he was God. The Gospels make it clear, though, that Jesus was the Christ, the Son of God. Just as he said he was.

We'll talk more about why we know that's true in this session.

The next question, though, is just as important: What difference does it make in your life?

Some people think it doesn't matter. Others refuse to "decide." Everyone is going to be held accountable, though, for what they have learned and how they have lived. And anyone living in the modern era, with access to the Internet, television, radio, and books has lost the excuse of ignorance.

What you believe about Jesus and how you live because of it have *eternal consequences* (as in, for all of eternity). This is huge.

If you were just a child, we wouldn't even be asking the question. You're not a child, though; you are a young man or a young woman. You are old enough to make an informed decision. It's time to grow up, spiritually, and ask some tough questions. It's also time to make some difficult decisions. No turning back.

The Lord is waiting for you with open arms. Let's take a step forward, today.

VERSE TO REMEMBER

"Jesus wept."

session 7:
Breaking It Down

1. Which of the Gospel writers were members of the original twelve apostles?_____

_____

2. Why did God send an angel to Mary? (Why not a prophet?)_____

_____

3. What does the word "disciple" mean?_____

4. Why does Jesus choose twelve apostles?_____

5. What does "parable" mean?_____

6. Why did Jesus have to die?_____

7. When do the Emmaus travelers recognize Jesus?_____

BRAIN TEASER

Name three consecutive days without using the words Wednesday, Friday, or Sunday.

The Triduum.

Creation ———▶ 2000 BC ———▶ 1700 BC ———▶ 1280 BC ———▶ 1240 BC ———▶ 1050 BC ———▶

EARLY WORLD	PATRIARCHS	EGYPT & EXODUS	DESERT WANDERINGS	CONQUEST & JUDGES	ROYAL KINGDOM
Genesis 1-11	Genesis 12-50	Exodus	Numbers	Joshua Judges	I & II Samuel I Kings 1-11

Gold
Gifts of the
Magi

Period 11: _____

Narrative Book: _____

who's who

1. _____

2. _____

3. _____

4. _____

DID YOU KNOW?

The word "Bethlehem" means "house of bread." Pretty cool that it's where the Bread of Life (John 6:35) was born, huh?

0 ────────────────► 33 AD

0 BC	722 BC	540 BC	167 BC		
DIVIDED KINGDOM I Kings 12-22 II Kings	**EXILE** II Kings	**RETURN** Ezra Nehemiah	**MACCABEAN REVOLT** I Maccabees	**MESSIANIC FULFILLMENT** Luke	**THE CHURCH** Acts

THE ROSARY,
YOUR FIRST BIBLE STUDY

Roll those beads!

What is the Rosary, and why do Catholics pray with beads?

The Rosary isn't just one of the most popular and famous forms of prayer for Catholics; it's one of the simplest ways to "pray" the Bible. When you pray the Rosary you're doing more than just reciting some Our Fathers and Hail Marys; you're thinking about (meditating on) the life of Jesus through the eyes of his Mother—our Mother, Mary.

(If you're wondering why Mary is also *our* Mother, check out John 19:27.)

Some early Christians (known as the "Desert Fathers") developed the structure for the Rosary, but St. Dominic usually gets the props for giving it to the greater, universal Catholic Church.

For centuries, the Rosary was divided into three sets of mysteries; joyful, sorrowful, and glorious. In 2002, Blessed John Paul II gave the Church the fourth set of mysteries, called the luminous mysteries.

The different mysteries of the Rosary focus on different events in the Bible. Each bead represents a simple prayer that even people with little or no formal education can remember. Each "decade" (or set of ten beads) represents a unique event in the lives of Christ and Mary, and all the beads together provide a kind of structured "prayer rhythm" that leads ordinary people closer to God.

When we pray the Rosary, we take our intentions to Mary and ask her to pray with us and for us. We show our honor and respect for her as the greatest of all the saints and as an example of perfect discipleship to us all.

When you pray a decade of the Rosary, try to put yourself "into" the event you are focusing on. Think about how characters like Mary or Peter were feeling when Christ acted and spoke. Use the Scripture verses to read the story for yourself as you begin each decade.

Each mystery has five decades, and each decade is prayed upon in the following order: one Our Father, ten Hail Marys, and one Glory Be. There are other prayers that are added onto the beginning and end of the Rosary, such as the Apostle's Creed and the Hail Holy Queen. See pages 38-39 for instructions on praying the Rosary.

Session Eight

● THE CHURCH

Book: Acts

Do you ever wonder what God wants for your future, what he designed you to do?

As we've heard throughout each of the previous sessions, God has a plan and you're in it. In fact, you're not just "in it"; your life also plays an important part in his plan of salvation. God wants to use you, as you've already heard, and he has a mission that only you can carry out.

The mission field where you are called to serve might change as you get older. God might take you to distant places or put you in unique settings. Your future mission field might include a seminary or a convent, medical school, or the military. Your future mission field might be in the corporate world or in ministry. Wherever the Lord leads you, he'll lead you to joy and fulfillment (if you actually let him lead, that is).

Right now, your mission field is a little closer to home. In fact, your home *is* your first mission field. You're called to share Christ's light first in your family. Your local parish is a mission field, too. You might think, "I'm too young" to have a mission, but you're not. In this session you'll hear about someone who thought the same way; God had big plans for him, just like he does for you.

After your family and your parish, your school is your next mission field. There are people there who need the One you know; they need Jesus. It's going to be your mission to share him with them. After that, your activities, from clubs to band to sports to dance to wherever you spend your time—all those rehearsals and practices, games, and meets—are mission field moments, times in which you can lead others closer to God through your witness.

God has been sending people on missions since the beginning of time, and in Scripture and in his Church, we get to know thousands of those souls well. Some people you'll read about here were born long before you were, but also read the same verses you are about to read … and did something about it.

What do you say? Are you up for a mission?

VERSE TO REMEMBER

"Let no one despise your youth, but set the believers an example in speech and conduct, in love, in faith, in purity."

---

session 8:
Breaking It Down

1. When did Jesus ascend into heaven?_____

2. What did the Jews celebrate on Pentecost?_____

3. What did the Holy Spirit allow Peter to do immediately after Pentecost?_____
    _____

4. Who was the first deacon to be martyred?_____

5. Why did God send Paul on tour?_____
    _____

6. How many missionary journeys did St. Paul go on?_____

DID YOU KNOW?

St. Paul was in a shipwreck on a boat with 276 people on board (Acts 27:37). In fact, Paul was shipwrecked three different times.

Creation	2000 BC	1700 BC	1280 BC	1240 BC	1050 BC

EARLY WORLD	PATRIARCHS	EGYPT & EXODUS	DESERT WANDERINGS	CONQUEST & JUDGES	ROYAL KINGDOM
Genesis 1-11	Genesis 12-50	Exodus	Numbers	Joshua Judges	I & II Samuel I Kings 1-11

Period 12: _____

Narrative Book: _____

White
the spotless
bride of Christ

who's who

1. ___Peter_____

2. _____

3. ___Timothy_____

*"Your only job from now on
is to become a Saint."*
−Mark Hart

33 AD ············

30 BC ──▶ 722 BC ──▶ 540 BC ·····▶ 167 BC ──────▶ 0 ─────────▶

DIVIDED KINGDOM
I Kings 12-22
II Kings

EXILE
II Kings

RETURN
Ezra
Nehemiah

MACCABEAN REVOLT
I Maccabees

MESSIANIC FULFILLMENT
Luke

THE CHURCH
Acts

GUIDE TO *LECTIO DIVINA*

So how do you "put yourself into the story" when you're reading the Bible, anyway?

Well, one of the best parts about being Catholic is that many different forms of prayer exist in our family history to help you.

For well more than a thousand years, Catholics have been praying the Scriptures with a prayer approach called *"lectio divina."* (It's a big Latin phrase that means "sacred reading.")

Have you ever had a conversation with a friend (boy or girl) that you like thinking about over and over again? Do you find yourself playing back the conversation in your head, remembering what was said, what you wish you hadn't said, what you feel you should have said, and all that? You probably even remember other details about it—where you were, how hot or cold it was, what music or movie was playing, maybe even what you were wearing. The more you think about it, breaking it down deeper and deeper, all those other details come to life in your head. Thinking deeply like that is called "contemplation." *Lectio divina* is something like that; it's a slow and intentional way of praying the Bible while talking to God. It's designed to help you become more *contemplative*.

So, what you do is take a short passage of Scripture (it's usually good to start in a Gospel) and follow four easy steps.

Historically, the four steps are known as:

1. ***Lectio*** (reading)

2. ***Meditatio*** (meditation)

3. ***Oratio*** (praying/speaking)

4. ***Contemplatio*** (contemplation)

BUT, since you probably don't speak Latin, it might be easier to remember the steps as:

1. **Read**

2. **Reflect**

3. **Respond**

4. **Rest**

Now, open your Bible, pick a Gospel story, and work through the four steps:

1. **Read**

   Select a passage and read it slowly. Get the basic "gist" of the story. Figure out the "who, what, when, where, why, and how" of it. After you've worked through it at least three or four times, you can move on to the next step.

2. **Reflect**

   Now, what is the main "point" of what you read? What words jumped out at you? Which words "spoke" to your heart? Was it comforting, or did the passage make you uncomfortable, and why? If nothing jumps out at you, read it again, and ask how the passage applies to you, today, living in the twenty-first century. If you don't think it applies to you, look harder. This is where you really chew on the Gospel and ask yourself some questions.

3. **Respond**

   Step three is where you and God speak together. If you're doing *lectio divina* alone, this is where you can *ask God questions* in your prayer. Anything that stood out to you in step two, bring to him now. Remember, it's important to listen in prayer, not just speak. Spend some time in silence and let God speak to your heart. Remember, this is about responding to God not only with your words, but with your heart. If you're doing *lectio divina* with a group, this is where you can discuss what the passage meant to you personally, what you liked, and what challenged you. Either way, it's important to listen to God speaking—to your heart or through other people.

4. **Rest**

   During this final step, you just "rest." Now, that might be difficult for you. Don't let yourself get distracted. Be sure you're removed from screens and noise. This is where you really become a child again. It's like you're crawling up onto your heavenly Father's lap and letting him hold you. It might take some "practice" at first, just to sit with God and let him love you. Picture God staring into your eyes. Imagine him telling you how proud he is of you. Let him remind you how much you mean to him and all he desires for you. The first three steps help you to slow down as you realize different things (dots); this fourth step is where God will connect those dots, if you let him.

CONTINUING THE JOURNEY

Use these steps to meditate on the "Great Verses for Young Men and Women" on pages 40-41.

MAJOR BIBLICAL EVENTS: NEW TESTAMENT REVIEW

An *Encounter* Cheat Sheet

The events listed below are not necessarily "more important" than others, but this list might help you track down some of the more famous scenes in the New Testament a little more quickly.

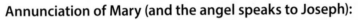

Annunciation of Mary (and the angel speaks to Joseph):

Luke 1:26-38

Matthew 1:18-25

Birth of Christ:

Luke 2:1-7

Presentation in the Temple:

Luke 2:22-29

Baptism in the River Jordan:

Matthew 3:13-17

Mark 1:9-11

Luke 3:21-22

Fasting and Temptation in the wilderness:

Matthew 4:1-11

Mark 1:12-13

Luke 4:1-13

Wedding at Cana:

John 2:1-12

Sermon on the Mount:

Matthew 5:1-12

Luke 6:17-49

Peter is given the keys:

Matthew 16:13-20

Transfiguration:

Matthew 17:1-9

Mark 9:2-9

Luke 9:28-36

Cleansing of the Temple:

John 2:13-17

The Last Supper:

Matthew 26:2-30

Mark 14:17-26

Luke 22:14-39

John 13:1-30

Jesus before Pilate:

Matthew 27:2, 11-31

Mark 15:1-5

Luke 23:1-17

John 18:28-40, 19:1-16

Crucifixion and Death:

Matthew 27:35-50

Mark 15:24-37

Luke 23:32-46

John 19:18-30

Resurrection:

Matthew 28:5-7

Mark 16:5-7

Luke 24:3-8

Ascension:

Mark 16:19

Luke 24:49-52

Pentecost:

Acts 2

Martyrdom of St. Stephen:

Acts 6–7

Conversion of St. Paul:

Acts 9:1-19

St. Paul's Missionary Journeys:

1. Acts 13–14

2. Acts 15:36–18:22

3. Acts 18:23–20:38

Additional Session Resources

THE TEN COMMANDMENTS

1. I AM THE LORD YOUR GOD. YOU SHALL WORSHIP THE LORD YOUR GOD AND HIM ONLY SHALL YOU SERVE.

2. YOU SHALL NOT TAKE THE NAME OF THE LORD YOUR GOD IN VAIN.

3. REMEMBER TO KEEP HOLY THE SABBATH DAY.

4. HONOR YOUR FATHER AND YOUR MOTHER.

5. YOU SHALL NOT KILL.

6. YOU SHALL NOT COMMIT ADULTERY.

7. YOU SHALL NOT STEAL.

8. YOU SHALL NOT BEAR FALSE WITNESS AGAINST YOUR NEIGHBOR.

9. YOU SHALL NOT COVET YOUR NEIGHBOR'S WIFE.

10. YOU SHALL NOT COVET YOUR NEIGHBOR'S GOODS.

It's important to realize that living by these commandments is more the "minimum" expectation of a Christian's ordinary, everyday behavior. Jesus reminds us of the importance of the Ten Commandments when he speaks to the rich young man (Matthew 19:16-22), but he also notes that the young man must surrender *everything* and follow him if he wants to experience eternal life.

Each of these commandments actually "covers" a variety of sins and warnings. Take some time to read through Part Three of the *Catechism of the Catholic Church*.

You might also notice that some Christians number the Ten Commandments differently than we Catholics do. The Catholic Tradition uses the division listed above, given to us by St. Augustine. Some Christian denominations number them differently. It's important to note, however, that this list is the one established by the early Church and handed on to us today.

If you can commit these to memory and live them out daily, you're well on your way to sainthood. Maybe you'll even get your own statue someday. (How cool would that be?)

EXAMINATION OF CONSCIENCE

In order to make a good confession, it's important to take time to do an examination of conscience. An examination is designed to help you recall anything and everything you've done that violated God's commandments, times when you failed to love God and others with your whole mind, heart, and strength.

Take some time to pray through the following questions, and give the Holy Spirit permission to reveal to your heart all those ways that you've fallen short of how God is calling you to live.

Spend some time repenting for your sins in your heart and preparing yourself to confess your sins during the sacrament of confession.

First and Second Commandments

"I am the LORD your God. You shall worship the Lord your God and him only shall you serve." "You shall not take the name of the Lord your God in vain." Do you blaspheme the name of God with your words and insults? Do you curse or use foul language against God or neighbor?

Third Commandment

"Remember to keep holy the Sabbath day." Do you intentionally miss Mass or holy days of obligation? Do you set aside necessary time on Sundays to rest and visit with family? Do you show reverence to God when you are in his house?

Fourth Commandment

"Honor your father and your mother." Do you disobey or disrespect your parents or other superiors? Do you neglect your responsibilities to your parents? Do you show your thanks and appreciation to your parents for all they do?

Fifth Commandment

"You shall not kill." Have you physically injured another person? Do you get angry or act maliciously toward others? Have you ever used alcohol or drugs or cut yourself? Have you ever participated in an abortion either directly or indirectly?

Sixth and Ninth Commandments

"You shall not commit adultery." "You shall not covet your neighbor's wife." Do you willingly entertain impure thoughts or desires? Do you use impure or suggestive language? Have you ever bought or viewed pornography? Have you ever committed impure acts with another or with yourself?

Eighth Commandment

"You shall not bear false witness against your neighbor." Do you intentionally lie? Do you deceive others or spread gossip? Do you fail to keep confidential information?

Seventh and Tenth Commandments

"You shall not steal." "You shall not covet your neighbor's goods." Have you ever stolen, cheated, or encouraged another to steal or cheat? Are you envious of other peoples' goods? Do you make getting material possessions the purpose of your life?

Act of Contrition

My God, I am sorry for my sins with all my heart. In choosing to do wrong and failing to do good, I have sinned against you whom I should love above all things. I firmly intend, with your help, to do penance, to sin no more, and to avoid whatever leads me to sin. Our Savior Jesus Christ suffered and died for us. In his name, my God, have mercy. Amen.

HOW TO PRAY THE ROSARY

The Rosary is a prayer directed to Jesus, through and with his Mother, Mary. The guided, scriptural prayers that we pray on the beads (the Our Father, Hail Mary, and Glory Be) help us pray. They are especially useful when your mind or body are tired or you can't seem to "find the right words" to pray. And remember that we must always keep in mind Jesus' warning not to let our prayers become repetitious babbling or empty phrases (Mt. 6:7).

Sometimes it helps to recite the prayers more slowly, to ensure we are *praying* and not just *saying* the prayers. So, grab your rosary beads and give it a try! Maybe start with just one decade and build from there. And as you begin, ask Mary to kneel beside you and pray with you—you'll be amazed at how much your relationship with Jesus grows through this awesome Catholic prayer.

1. **Make the Sign of the Cross**

2. **Pray the Apostles Creed -** Crucifix

   I believe in God, the Father Almighty, Creator of heaven and earth, and in Jesus Christ, his only Son, our Lord, who was conceived by the Holy Spirit, born of the Virgin Mary, suffered under Pontius Pilate, was crucified, died and was buried; he descended into hell; on the third day he rose again from the dead; he ascended into heaven, and is seated at the right hand of God, the Father Almighty; from there he will come to judge the living and the dead. I believe in the Holy Spirit, the holy catholic Church, the communion of saints, the forgiveness of sins, the resurrection of the body, and life everlasting. Amen.

3. **Pray an Our Father –** 1st bead

   Our Father, who art in heaven, hallowed be thy name; thy kingdom come; thy will be done on earth as it is in heaven. Give us this day our daily bread; and forgive us our trespasses as we forgive those who trespass against us; and lead us not into temptation, but deliver us from evil. Amen.

4. **Pray three Hail Marys –** 2nd through 4th beads

   Hail Mary, full of grace, the Lord is with you; blessed are you among women, and blessed is the fruit of your womb, Jesus. Holy Mary, Mother of God, pray for us sinners now and at the hour of our death. Amen.

5. **Pray a Glory Be and the (optional) Fatima Prayer –** 5th bead

   Glory be to the Father, the Son, and the Holy Spirit; as it was in the beginning, is now, and ever shall be, world without end. Amen.

   O my Jesus, forgive us our sins, save us from the fires of hell, lead all souls to heaven, especially those in most need of thy mercy.

6. **Announce the first mystery, then pray the Our Father.**

7. **Pray ten Hail Marys while meditating on the mystery on the next ten beads (a "decade").**

8. **When you get to the next single bead, pray the Glory Be and the (optional) Fatima Prayer. Announce the second mystery while on the same bead.**

9. **Repeat steps 6-8 for each of the three remaining mysteries.**

10. **After you've finished the fifth mystery and are back to the center piece, finish the Rosary by praying the Hail Holy Queen …**

Hail, holy Queen, mother of mercy, our life, our sweetness, and our hope. To you we cry, poor banished children of Eve; to you we send up our sighs, mourning and weeping in this valley of tears.

Turn, then, most gracious advocate, your eyes of mercy toward us; and after this, our exile, show unto us the blessed fruit of your womb, Jesus. O clement, O loving, O sweet Virgin Mary.

Leader: *Pray for us, O Holy Mother of God …*

All: *That we may be made worthy of the promises of Christ.*

Leader: *Let us pray.*

All: *O God, whose only begotten Son, by his life, death, and resurrection, has purchased for us the rewards of eternal life; grant, we beseech thee, that meditating upon these mysteries of the Most Holy Rosary of the Blessed Virgin Mary, we may imitate what they contain and obtain what they promise, through the same Christ our Lord. Amen.*

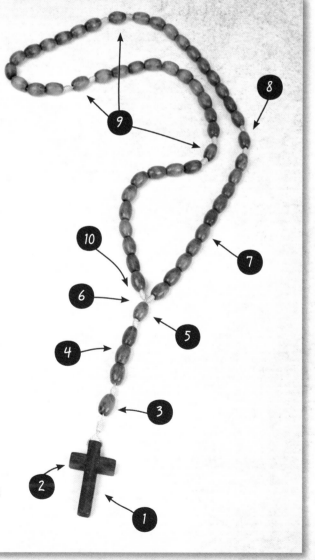

Joyful Mysteries (Monday, Saturday)
The Annunciation: Luke 1:26-33, 38
The Visitation: Luke 1:39-45
The Nativity of Jesus: Luke 2:6-12
The Presentation of Jesus: Luke 2:25-32
The Finding of Jesus: Luke 2:41-50

Sorrowful Mysteries (Tuesday, Friday)
The Agony in the Garden: Luke 22:39-46
The Scourging at the Pillar: Mark 15:6-15
The Crowning with Thorns: John 19:1-8
The Carrying of the Cross: John 19:16-22
The Crucifixion: John 19:25-30

Glorious Mysteries (Wednesday, Sunday)
The Resurrection: Mark 16:1-7
The Ascension of Jesus: Luke 24:45-53
The Descent of the Holy Spirit: Acts 2:1-7, 11
The Assumption of Mary: Luke 1:46-55
The Coronation of Mary: Revelation 12:1-7

Luminous Mysteries (Thursday)
The Baptism of Jesus: Matthew 3:13-17
The Miracle at Cana: John 2:1-11
The Proclamation of the Kingdom: Mark 1:14-15
The Transfiguration: Matthew 17:1-8
The Institution of the Eucharist: Matthew 26:26-28

It might be difficult for you to pray the Rosary at first. I'll be honest with you—even though I pray it daily, it can still be tough because the soothing repetition can almost put you to sleep sometimes. The rhythm can be both a good thing and a bad thing (if you're like me). I have to work very hard to stay focused. Kneeling helps.

Continuing Your Journey

GREAT VERSES FOR YOUNG MEN

"Likewise urge the younger men to control themselves. Show yourself in all respects a model of good deeds, and in your teaching show integrity, gravity, and sound speech that cannot be censured, so that an opponent may be put to shame, having nothing evil to say of us" **(Titus 2:6-8).**

"Do your best to present yourself to God as one approved, a workman who has no need to be ashamed, rightly handling the word of truth" **(2 Timothy 2:15).**

"Let no evil talk come out of your mouths, but only such as is good for edifying, as fits the occasion, that it may impart grace to those who hear" **(Ephesians 4:29).**

"But I am afraid that as the serpent deceived Eve by his cunning, your thoughts will be led astray from a sincere and pure devotion to Christ" **(2 Corinthians 11:3).**

"I appeal to you therefore, brethren, by the mercies of God, to present your bodies as a living sacrifice, holy and acceptable to God, which is your spiritual worship. Do not be conformed to this world but be transformed by the renewal of your mind, that you may prove what is the will of God, what is good and acceptable and perfect" **(Romans 12:1-2).**

"For all that is in the world, the lust of the flesh and the lust of the eyes and the pride of life, is not of the Father but is of the world. And the world passes away, and the lust of it; but he who does the will of God abides for ever" **(1 John 2:16-17).**

"Finally, brethren, whatever is true, whatever is honorable, whatever is just, whatever is pure, whatever is lovely, whatever is gracious, if there is any excellence, if there is anything worthy of praise, think about these things" **(Philippians 4:8).**

GREAT VERSES FOR YOUNG WOMEN

"Charm is deceitful, and beauty is vain, but a woman who fears the Lord is to be praised" **(Proverbs 31:30).**

"Therefore encourage one another and build one another up, just as you are doing" **(1 Thessalonians 5:11).**

"Know this, my beloved brethren. Let every man be quick to hear, slow to speak, slow to anger, for the anger of man does not work the righteousness of God" **(James 1:19-20).**

"Let not yours be the outward adorning with braiding of hair, decoration of gold, and wearing of robes, but let it be the hidden person of the heart with the imperishable jewel of a gentle and quiet spirit, which in God's sight is very precious" **(1 Peter 3:3-4).**

"Not that I complain of want; for I have learned, in whatever state I am, to be content" **(Philippians 4:11).**

"Shun immorality. Every other sin which a man commits is outside the body; but the immoral man sins against his own body. Do you not know that your body is a temple of the Holy Spirit within you, which you have from God? You are not your own; you were bought with a price. So glorify God in your body" **(1 Corinthians 6:18-20).**

"For this is the will of God, your sanctification: that you abstain from immorality. … For God has not called us for uncleanness, but in holiness. Therefore whoever disregards this, disregards not man but God, who gives his Holy Spirit to you" **(1 Thessalonians 4:3, 7-8).**

"For I know the plans I have for you, says the Lord, plans for welfare and not for evil, to give you a future and a hope" **(Jeremiah 29:11).**

THE WORD FOR THE DAY

Living the Catholic life isn't easy. Being a Christian in today's world requires a lot of patience with challenging people and constant prayer for people, especially those within your own family. Below is a list of different emotions, feelings, struggles, or challenges that you will face on a daily or weekly basis, as well as a passage from the Bible that might offer you some hope, direction, and insight. Happy reading!

Worried about what your future holds? **Jeremiah 29:11**

Can't find the "right words" when you pray? **Matthew 6:9-15**

Feeling like no one will listen to you because you're too young? **1 Timothy 4:12**

Down on yourself because you keep messing up? **Romans 3:23**

Concerned that God has "abandoned" you? **Matthew 28:20**

Are you afraid to confess your sins? **1 John 1:9**

What should you do about your "enemies"? **Luke 6:35**

Need confidence before you start your day? **Psalms 62:1-2**

Nothing you do … nothing, can make God love you less. **Romans 8:38-39**

Are you tired of "doing the right thing"? **2 Thessalonians 3:13**

Are you overwhelmed by temptation? **1 Corinthians 10:13**

Want to know the secret to being "great" in God's eyes? **Luke 22:26**

Feeling tired or weak? **Isaiah 40:28-31**

Feeling alone or down? **Joshua 1:9**

Do you ever feel like just "losing it" with someone? **Proverbs 13:3-4**

Why be holy? **1 Peter 1:15-16**

Ever wonder if God is really listening to your prayers? **Jeremiah 29:12**

Have you been hurt by others' actions? **2 Corinthians 12:20**

Are you afraid to trust God with your whole life? **Romans 9:33**

Is remaining pure a struggle for you or your friends? **1 Thessalonians 4:7**

Have you "given up" on certain friends or family ever following God? **Matthew 19:26**

AWFUL BIBLE JOKES

Q: What kind of man was Boaz before he got married?
A: Ruth-less.

Q: At what time of day was Adam created?
A: A little before Eve.

Q: Where was the first math problem mentioned in the Bible?
A: In Genesis, when God told Adam and Eve to go forth and multiply.

Q: On the ark, Noah probably got milk from the cows onboard. What did he get from the ducks?
A: Quackers.

Q: Which animal on Noah's ark had the highest level of intelligence?
A: The giraffe.

Q: When was the first lunch meat mentioned in the Bible?
A: When Noah took Ham into the ark.

Q: How many people went on board the ark before Noah?
A: Three, because it says "Noah went forth" (Genesis 8:18).

Q: Why was everyone in biblical times so poor?
A: Because there was only one Job.

Q: How long did Cain dislike his brother?
A: As long as he was Abel.

Q: What was Noah's greatest worry?
A: The pair of termites.

Q: Who was the greatest comedian in the Bible?
A: Samson. He brought the house down.

Q: Why couldn't Noah's wife and sons play cards on the ark?
A: Because Noah sat on the deck.

Q: The ark was built in three stories, and the top story had a window to let light in, but how did they get light to the bottom two stories?
A: They used floodlights.

Q: What do they call pastors in Germany?
A: German Shepherds.

Q: Who was the most flagrant lawbreaker in the Bible?
A: Moses. Because he broke all ten commandments at once.

Q: Which Bible character had no parents?
A: Joshua, son of Nun.

Q: Where was Solomon's temple located?
A: On the side of his head.

Q: Which Old Testament character was known for having a foul mouth at a young age?
A: Job—he cursed the day he was born (Job 3:1).

Q: What do you call a sleepwalking nun?
A: A roamin' Catholic!

HOW WELL DO YOU KNOW THE BIBLE?

Across

1. What did Jesus give Peter to represent his papal authority?
3. When did three apostles see Jesus with Moses and Elijah?
5. What archangel fought the devil in Revelation 12?
10. What was Mary's mother's name?
12. The Greek word for "witness" is _____.
13. Who did Jesus raise from the dead after four days?
14. What did Jesus change Simon's name to?
15. She was Moses' sister.
17. Where did Jesus perform his first miracle?
18. This man climbed a tree to get a better view of Jesus.
19. What was the name of the garden where Jesus was arrested?
22. Who told Mary she would conceive a son?
24. What was the name of the apostle who succeeded Judas?
25. Where did Jesus grow up?
26. How many sons did Noah have?
27. This king sought to kill the baby Jesus.
28. On what feast did the Holy Spirit descend upon the apostles?
29. Christ quoted this psalm from the cross.

Down

2. What king followed King David?
4. How many loaves of bread did Jesus multiply?
6. He was Moses' brother.
7. Jesus worked as a _____.
8. What river did God turn to blood (in Exodus 7)?
9. What was the name of the criminal Pilate released in Jesus' place?
11. Who was Mary's cousin, the mother of John the Baptist?
16. This list begins: "Blessed are the poor …"
19. Who did David fight with a slingshot?
20. What was the name of the garden where Adam and Eve lived?
21. What was the name of Abraham's wife?
23. Which apostle was a tax collector?

Answers on page 48

WHO'S WHO IN THE BIBLE?

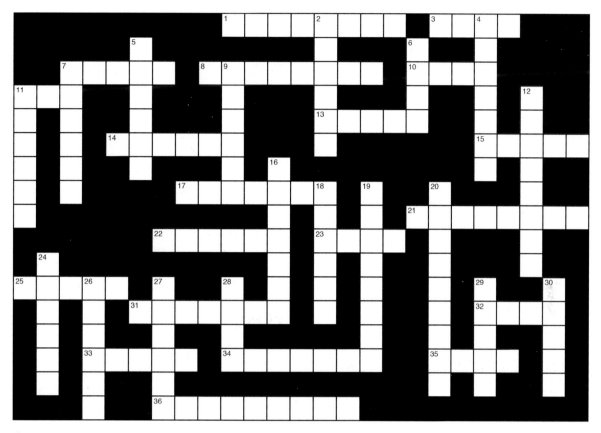

Across

1. This prophet was a young man when God called him.
3. He was Eve's third son.
7. Who was swallowed by a large fish?
8. Moses' wife's name was _____.
10. He was Eve's husband.
11. Adam's wife was _____.
13. Moses' brother's name was _____.
14. Who "took over" after Moses?
15. This king sought to kill the baby Jesus.
17. What Philistine warrior battled David?
21. He was released (by Pilate) instead of Jesus.
22. What queen saved her people?
23. God warned him about the Flood.
25. What shepherd slayed the giant?
31. This angel battled the devil.
32. She is the first prophetess mentioned in the New Testament.
33. His name means "laughter."
34. Jesus raised this good friend from the dead.
35. He married the widow, Ruth.
36. This cousin of Mary proclaimed her "Blessed …"

Down

2. Moses' sister's name was _____.
4. Paul wrote to this young bishop.
5. Who is the Bible's "strongest man"?
6. He was Eve's first son.
7. Moses' father-in-law was named _____.
9. God changed Jacob's name to _____.
11. This prophet took on the "prophets" of Baal.
12. He was Mark's cousin and traveled with Paul.
16. This angel visited Mary.
18. Her son, Samuel, became a mighty prophet.
19. This apostle also went by the name Jude.
20. She was the wife of David and the mother of Solomon.
24. She was Isaac's wife and Leah's little sister.
26. This prophet's book is the longest.
27. This leader "washed his hands" of Jesus.
28. St. Paul was first known as _____.
29. She saved her family's lives in Jericho.
30. She was Abraham's wife.

Answers on page 48

DID YOU KNOW?

1. Israelites were forbidden (in Old Testament times) to wear clothes made of two kinds of material. So much for 50 percent cotton and 50 percent polyester!

2. The word "manna" literally means, "What is it?"

3. There weren't just two of every animal on the ark. In fact, there were seven pairs of all the clean animals (Genesis 7:2-4).

4. In 2 Samuel 21:20-21, it says that Jonathan killed a man who had six fingers on each hand and six toes on each foot. Seriously.

5. King David had twenty children (1 Chronicles 3:1-9). They probably didn't go out to eat very much.

6. Abraham was 100 years old when his son, Isaac, was born (Genesis 21:5). Imagine him trying to keep up at the playground.

7. St. Paul and the early Christian disciples would pray every day at 3 PM (Acts 3:1). Many people still do it.

8. King Solomon had 12,000 horses (1 Kings 10:26). Imagine the smell.

9. King Solomon imported peacocks to decorate his palace (1 Kings 10:22). Throw pillows probably would have been less messy.

10. Job had 3,000 camels (Job 1:3) … animals, not cigarettes.

11. St. Paul was in a shipwreck on a boat with 276 people on board (Acts 27:37). In fact, Paul was shipwrecked three different times.

12. The Garden of Eden had four different rivers: Pishon, Gihon, Tigris, and Euphrates (Genesis 2:11-14). Any of those sound familiar from social studies?

BRAIN TEASERS

1. After a prank went wrong, a student was told, "If you tell a lie, you will get suspended; if you tell the truth, you will still get a detention." What could he say to avoid both?

2. How far can Jesus travel into the desert?

3. What do these three sentences have in common that is usually uncommon?
   - Saints don't punch animals.
   - A saint is a good Catholic.
   - It is unusual to think of a story about a Catholic saint who ran into a volcano.

4. What was given to you that others use more than you do, but that can't get used up?

5. What binds two people, is used by one, and is seen by all?

6. Speak its name aloud and it disappears. What is it?

7. Remove three letters from this sequence to reveal a famous saint: THAREUEGLUESTTTIERNSE

8. Sister Teresa bets Sister Mary that whatever Sister Mary can pull in a wagon halfway up a hill, she can pull all the way up the hill. How can Sister Mary win the bet?

9. How can you spell reconciliation using only five different letters?

10. What does a priest change daily, yet never looks different?

Answers on page 49

Answer Key

HOW WELL DO YOU KNOW THE BIBLE? (FROM PAGE 44)

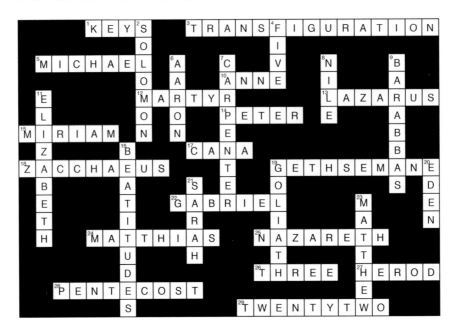

WHO'S WHO IN THE BIBLE? (FROM PAGE 45)

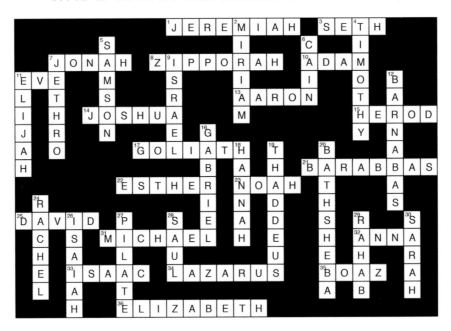

BRAIN TEASERS - ANSWERS (FROM PAGE 47)

1. *"You will suspend me."*

2. *Halfway. After that, he will be traveling out of the desert.*

3. *They don't have any "E's" in them.*

4. *Your name.*

5. *Wedding ring.*

6. *Silence.*

7. *Augustine (remove THREE LETTERS).*

8. *Pull Sister Teresa in the wagon.*

9. *Mercy.*

10. *Bread and wine.*

THE DIVINE DESIGNER ENDNOTES (FROM PAGE 8)

1 CK-12 Foundation, *CK-12.org*, ck12.org/book/CK-12-Biology-Concepts/r11/, October 16, 2012.

2 Charles Q. Choi and Jeanna Bryner, Ed., "Brute Force: Humans Can Sure Take a Punch," *LiveScience*, livescience.com/6040-brute-force-humans-punch.html, October 16, 2012.

3 Ed Grabianowski, "How many skin cells do you shed every day?" *HowStuffWorks.com*, *Discovery Fit and Health*, health.howstuffworks.com/skin-care/information/anatomy/shed-skin-cells.html, October 17, 2012.

4 Georgia State University, *HyperPhysics*, hyperphysics.phy-astr.gsu.edu/hbase/vision/rodcone.html, October 16, 2012.

5 Sue Caldwell, "Renal (Kidney) Physiology," Grossmont College, grossmont.edu/suecaldwell/141_excretory.htm, 2012._

6 Vogt, "Introduction to Astronomy: The Tilt of the Earth," New Mexico State University, web.nmsu.edu/~esgerken/lecture07/slide04.html, 2009.

7 The Library of Congress, *Library of Congress Online*, loc.gov/rr/scitech/mysteries/snowcrystals.html, October 17, 2012.

8 David Wallechinsky and Amy Wallace, *The People's Almanac* (Melbourne, New York: CANONGATE, 1986).

9 W.C. Lindemann and C.R. Glover, "Nitrogen Fixation by Legumes," New Mexico State University and the US Department of Agriculture, May 2003.

10 United States Department of Commerce, *National Ocean Service*, oceanservice.noaa.gov/facts/oceandepth.html, October 16, 2012.

11 Fraser Cain, "What Percentage of the Earth's Land Surface is Desert?" *Universe Today*, universetoday.com/65639/what-percentage-of-the-earths-land-surface-is-desert/, June 1, 2010.

12 US Geological Survey, The USGS Water Science School, ga.water.usgs.gov/edu/earthhowmuch.html, October 16, 2012.

13 Nicholas Wethington, "How many stars are in the Milky Way," *Universe Today*, universetoday.com/22380/how-many-stars-are-in-the-milky-way/, December 16, 2008.

Notes

Notes

Notes